The Complete Illustrated

THORBURN'S MAMMALS

The Complete Illustrated
THORBURN'S
MAMMALS

Illustrated by
ARCHIBALD THORBURN

with an Introduction and Notes by
Dr Gordon B. Corbet

BEAVER
PUBLISHING

This edition published in Great Britain by
Beaver Publishing Limited
Alderley Edge, Cheshire, SK9 7DT. 1997

Beaver Publishing is an imprint of Ravette Publishing Limited

ISBN 1 85962 057 4

Designed by Robert Mathias, Publishing Workshop

Printed and bound by
Artes Graficas Elkar, Bilbao, Spain

INTRODUCTION

THE BRITISH MAMMAL FAUNA is small by most standards. Thorburn was thorough but not completely comprehensive in depicting 72 species, and several of these are rare vagrants like the Arctic seals. But mammals are exceedingly diverse: in size, in appearance and in way of life. Compare for example a pipistrelle bat with a red deer; a harvest mouse with a humpback whale; a weasel with a grey seal. Throughout history this diversity has been reflected in man's attitude to wild mammals. Some, like the rats, have always been treated as pests; others as a valued resource for meat, sport or fur, while many fall equivocally between or amongst several of these categories. Such attitudes to wildlife not only vary from place to place and from person to person, but they have also changed with time.

Archibald Thorburn produced his *British mammals* in 1920/21 at a pivotal time when attitudes were changing fast, driven by social and economic changes and the accelerating progress of scientific knowledge. Thorburn was primarily an illustrator of birds, beginning with a significant contribution to Walter Swaysland's modest *Familiar wild birds* (4 slim volumes, 1883-4), followed by Lord Lilford's monumental *Coloured figures of the birds of the British Isles* (7 volumes, 1885-98). His first major venture in the illustration of mammals was in *The mammals of Great Britain and Ireland* by J G Millais (3 volumes, 1904-6), to which he contributed 30 colour plates.

Throughout that period, through Victorian and Edwardian times, British natural history, at least in so far as it dealt with mammals and birds, was dominated by the sporting aristocracy and their followers, with the cult of red deer stalking in the Scottish Highlands, and widespread preservation of game birds accompanied by the attempt to suppress any species, bird or mammal, that appeared to conflict in any way with sport. Even amongst those motivated by scientific curiosity rather than the hunting instinct, this was an era of collecting, and the naturalist interested in birds or mammals would feel naked without a gun.

The war of 1914-18 imposed many changes — gamekeeping was relaxed, resulting in the beginning of recovery of some of the predatory species that had been driven close to extinction, including the wild cat, pine marten and polecat. Many sporting estates were broken up, some to provide the newly formed Forestry Commission with land to plant for a strategic reserve of timber. The study of British birds and mammals had also reached a stage when they were well enough known that the shooting and collecting of specimens was no longer a constructive and satisfying way for the amateur naturalist to add to knowledge.

In 1912 the publication by the British Museum (Natural History) of G S Miller's *Catalogue of the mammals of Western Europe* (a detailed descriptive work, not just an inventory of specimens as might be assumed from the title) put the classification of British mammals on a basis that was not only far in advance of anything that had gone before but must have seemed close to being definitive.

In ornithology, pioneering work was in progress that would move the study of birds from the museum to the field: Julian Huxley's study of courtship in grebes; Eliot Howard's painstaking elucidation of the nature of territory in warblers; and the photographic innovations of pioneers like the Kearton brothers. The advance of photographic technology also affected the process of colour printing, and Thorburn's *British mammals* was one of the first works to be printed from water-colour originals through a photographic process.

In his artwork Thorburn reflected the period in drawing from nature where practical and in placing his subjects in natural settings. Only his wild cat (Plate 10) has echoes of an earlier era, portraying it as terrified and 'at bay', as if peering into the barrel of a gun. And of course the era of underwater photography of whales had not begun and he was obliged to base his drawings of whales and dolphins on the models in the Natural History Museum, many of which were in turn based upon rather flimsy evidence as to the appearance of the living animals. In his text Thorburn drew heavily upon Millais' work of 1904/6, and although quoting from the more recent works of Barrett-Hamilton's *History of British mammals* begun in 1910, in choosing scientific names he curiously hearkened back to Millais and 19th century authors.

Following 1920/21 there was a period when rather little interest was shown in the natural history of British mammals. Not until after the war of 1939-45 was there a resurgence of interest, sparked by the publication of L Harrison Matthews' *British mammals* in Collins' *New naturalist* series (1952). This, coupled with the pioneering work of the Oxford ecologists under Charles Elton, led to a massive surge of interest in studying mammals in the field, including the formation of the Mammal Society in 1954.

It was under the umbrella of the Mammal Society that successive editions of the *Handbook of British mammals* have been produced (1964, 1977, 1991), each one quickly becoming out of date as new information flowed in. This new information came increasingly from professional zoologists, although many dedicated amateurs have continued to make valuable contributions. Today our knowledge of how mammals conduct their lives, especially at night when most of them are active, is enhanced by the use of a whole battery of modern technology — infrared cameras to penetrate the darkness; micro-electronics to attach radio-transmitters to even the smallest mouse; DNA fingerprinting to establish paternity and elucidate social structure; satellites to track the movements of oceanic whales. However Thorburn would have been heartened to know that despite these and the excellence of colour photography, modern field guides to mammals still depend upon the talent and artistry of illustrators working as he did with paint and brush.

CONTENTS

THE PLATES

Greater Horseshoe Bat. Lesser Horseshoe Bat. ⅔

Long-eared Bat.
Barbastelle.

2/3.

Pl. 3

Pipistrelle or Common Bat.

Noctule.

Pl. 2

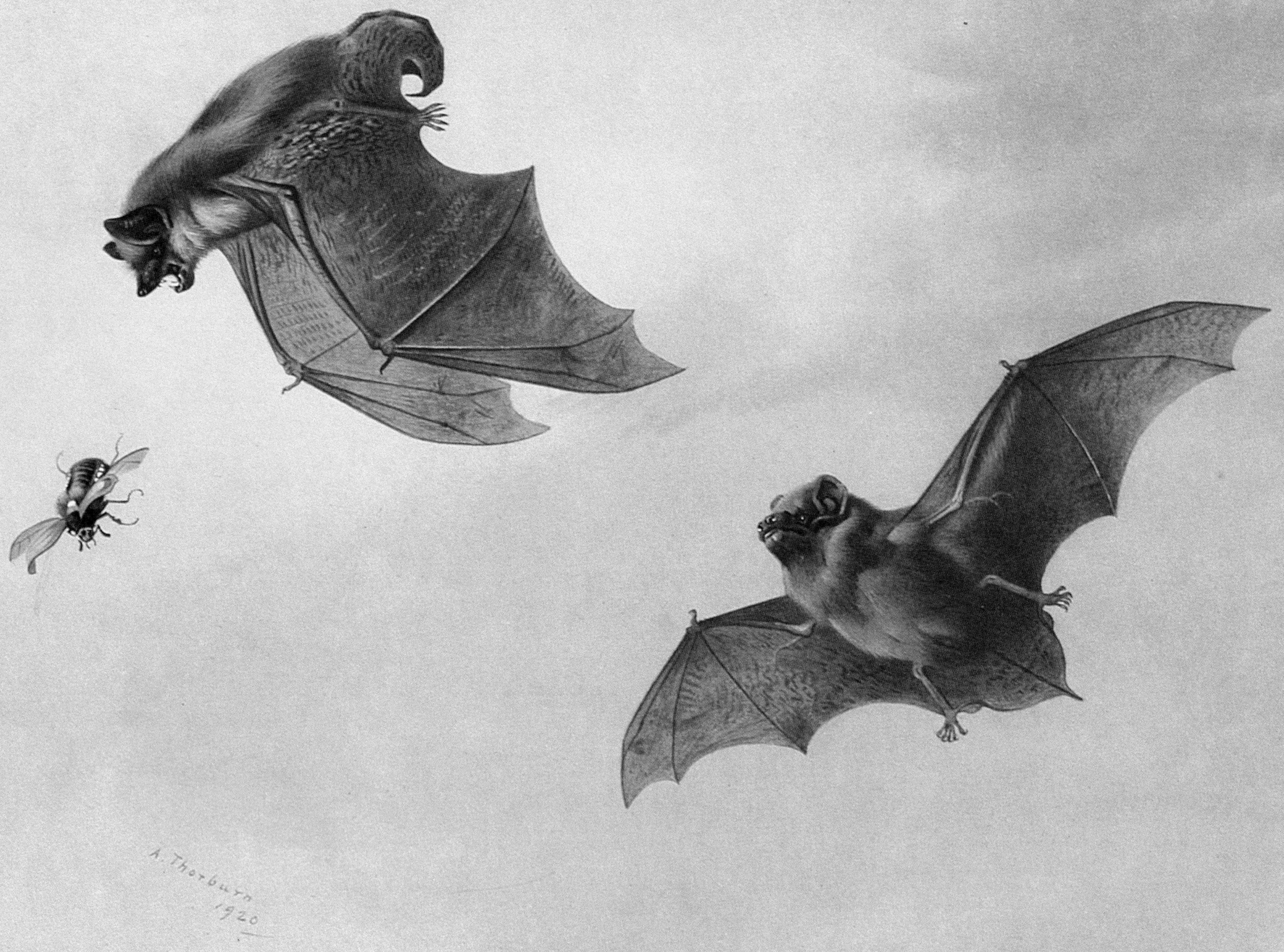
A. Thorburn
1920

Serotine. Leisler's Bat. $\frac{2}{3}$

Pl.5.

Natterer's Bat.

Pl. 7.

Hedgehog. ♂.

Mole.

$\frac{2}{3}$

A. Thorburn
1918

PL 8

Pl. 9

Common Shrew.   Lesser Shrew

Water Shrew.

$\frac{3}{4}$

Wild Cat. ⅓

FOX

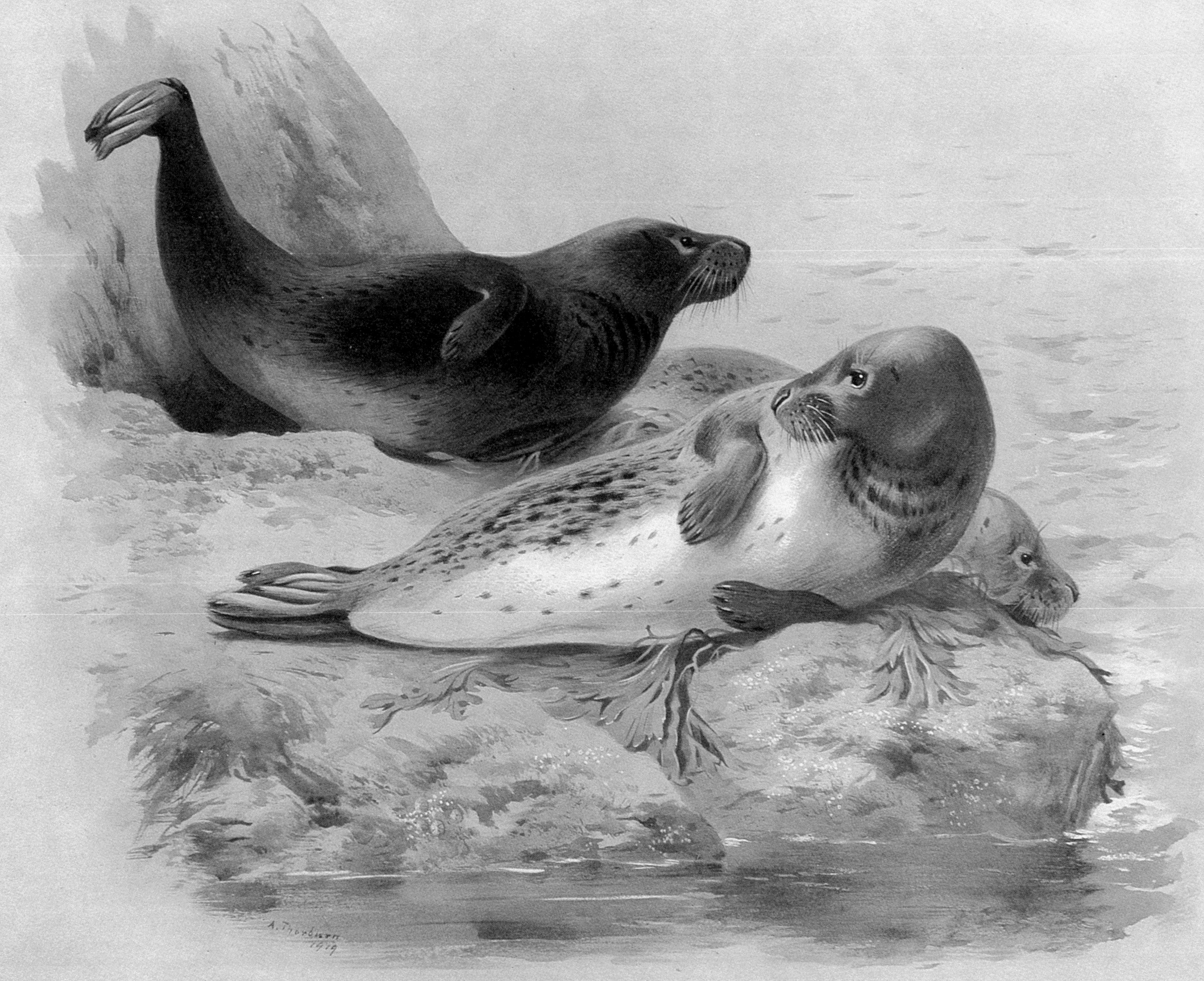

Grey Seal. 1/12

Common Seal. 72.

Pl.14.

Pl. 15

Ringed Seal.   Harp Seal.

$\frac{1}{12}$

Pl. 16

Hooded Seal. (adult & young.)

1/12

Bearded Seal.

Otter. ⅓

Badger. $\frac{2}{7}$.

Pl. 1

Pine Marten. $\frac{1}{2}$.

Polecat. $\frac{2}{7}$.

Thorburn 1918

Pl 21.

Stoat. (winter) ½

Pl.23

Pl. 2

Squirrel ½

A. Thorburn 1919.

Pl.2

Dormouse. $\frac{3}{4}$.

Pl. 2.

Harvest Mouse.
Wood Mouse. $\frac{3}{4}$

Pl.2

Yellow-necked Wood Mouse.
St. Kilda Wood Mouse. ¾

Pl.2

St. Kilda House Mouse.

Common Mouse. $\frac{3}{4}$

Pl. 29

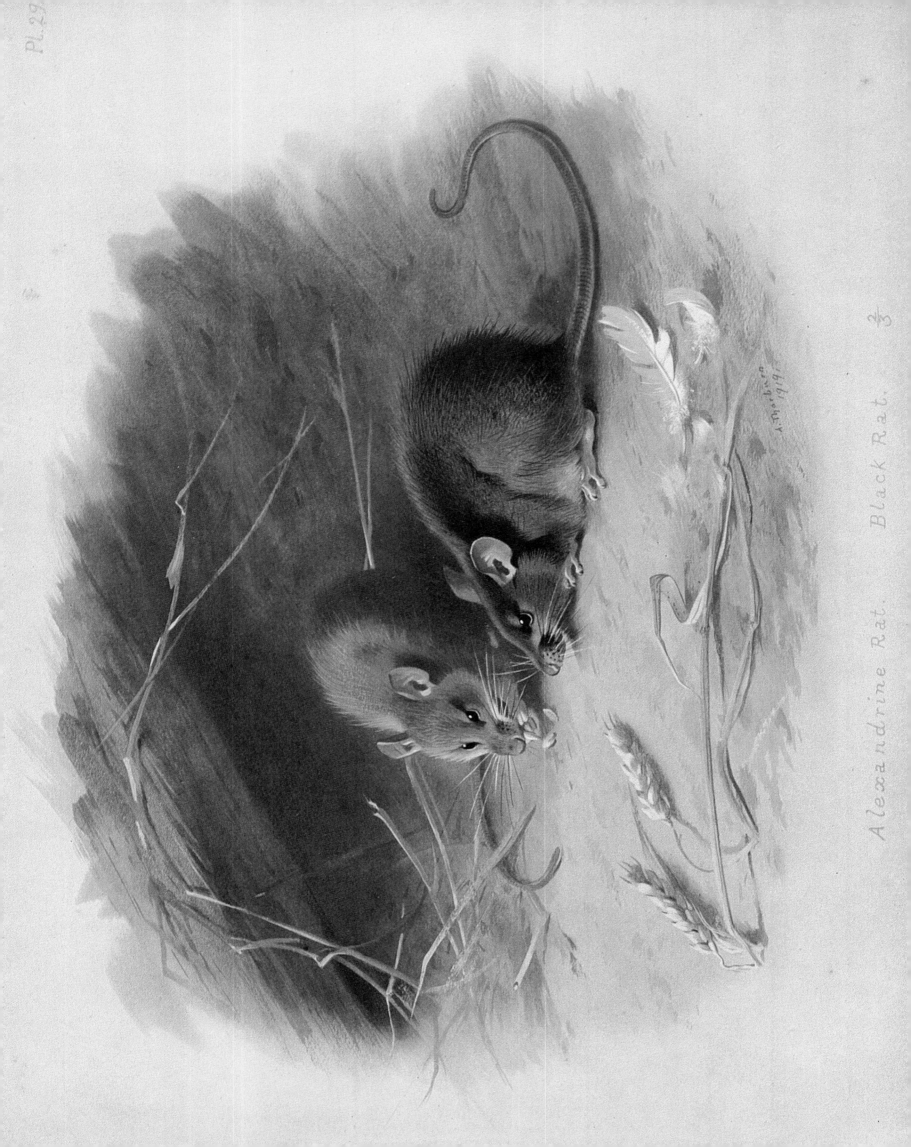

Pl. 30

Brown Rat. 2/3.

A. Thorburn. 1918

Pl. 31.

Field-Vole.   Bank Vole.
                Orkney Vole.   3/4

Pl. 3

Water Vole. $\frac{2}{3}$

Common Hare. ⅓

Pl. 34

Mountain Hare. (autumn)

Irish Hare.

A. Thorburn 1914

Pl. 35.

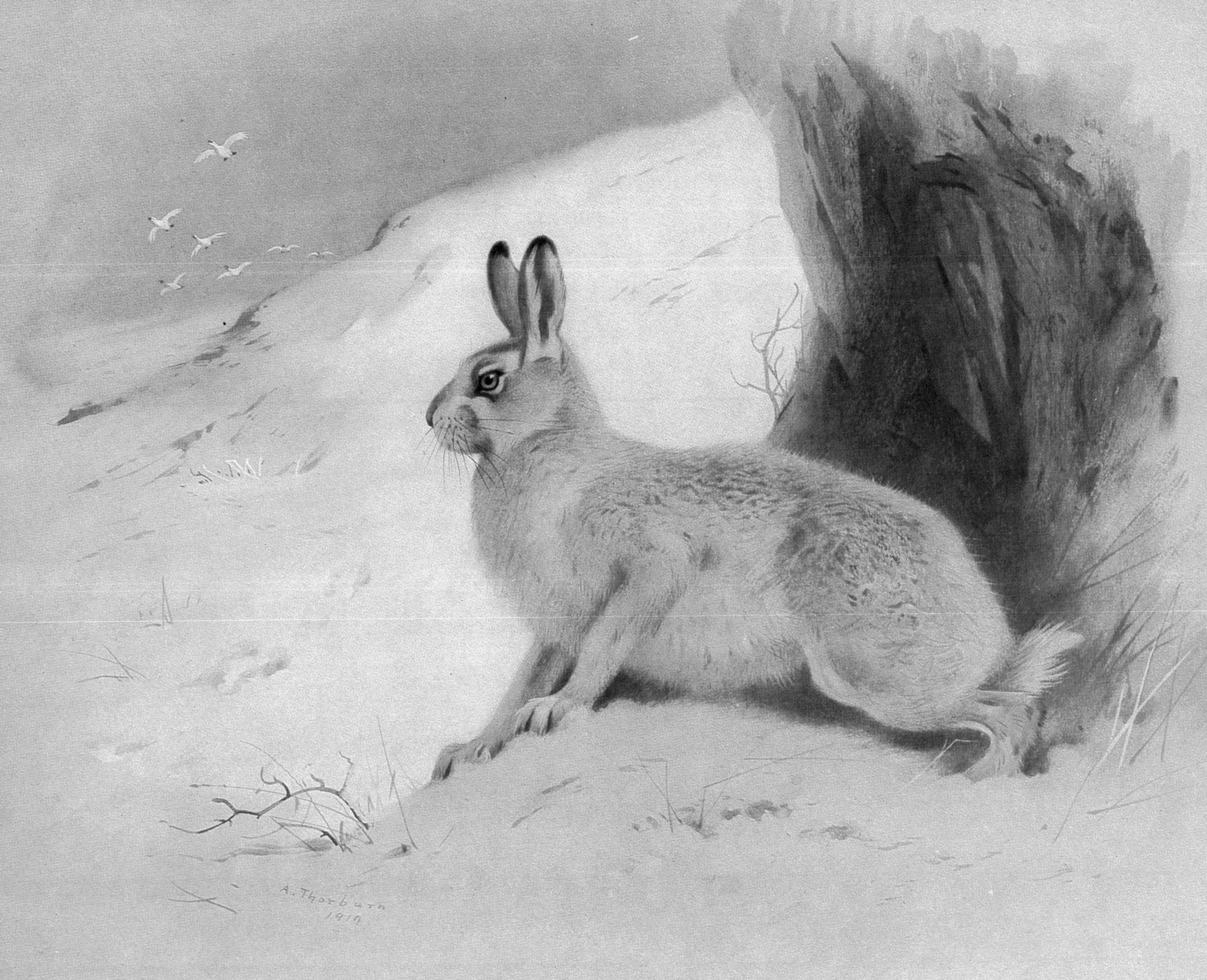
A. Thorburn
1919

Mountain Hare. (winter) 1/3

Rabbit. $\frac{2}{3}$.

A. Thorburn. 1919.

Pl.36

Pl. 37

Red Deer. $\frac{1}{12}$

Fallow Deer ♂

Roe Deer. ⁴⁄

Wild Cattle. Cadzow.

A. Thorburn 1916

Pl.41.

Chillingham Bull.

Chartley Bull.

Atlantic Right Whale.

Humpbacked Whale.

$\frac{1}{75}$

Pl.45

Common Rorqual

Sibbald's Rorqual or Blue Whale. 80.

Lesser Rorqual
Rudolphi's Rorqual.
60

Bottle-nosed Whale.
11

Pl.45.

Bottle-nosed Whale.

Sperm Whale. 60

Sowerby's Whale.

25.

Cuvier's Whale.

Pl. 46.

Pl. 47.

White Whale.
Narwhal. $\frac{1}{30}$

Pl. 48

Killer.
Pilot Whale. $\frac{1}{38}$.

Pl. 49.

Porpoise. $\frac{1}{15}$

Risso's Grampus. $\frac{1}{17}$
(after Flower) Trans. Zool. Soc.

White-sided Dolphin $\frac{1}{15}$

Pl. 5

White-beaked Dolphin.

Bottle-nosed Dolphin.

Common Dolphin. 1/5

NOTES ON THE PLATES

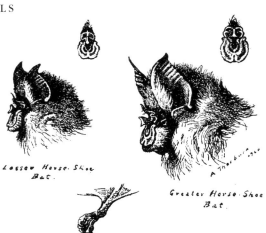

Lesser Horse-Shoe Bat.

Greater Horse-Shoe Bat.

──── PLATE 1 ────

Horseshoe bats

Horseshoe bats differ from all the other British bats in having a complex of fleshy lobes around the nostrils, including a horseshoe-shaped lower flange, part of their equipment for navigation by echo-location. The pulses of ultrasonic sound used for echo-location are emitted through the nostrils and modulated by the noseleaves. At rest they wrap their wings around their bodies as they hang freely from the roof of a cave or tunnel (in winter) or sometimes the attic of a building in summer.

Like all European bats they feed exclusively on insects caught mainly in flight and they hibernate during the winter. They breed in colonies; mating takes place in autumn with births (single) in June or July. The young can fly at an age of about three weeks and are weaned by about five weeks. Like most bats they are long-lived, over 20 years in the case of some greater horseshoes.

Greater horseshoe bat
Rhinolophus ferrumequinum
One of the largest of British bats, with a wingspan around 34-38 cm. Once widespread in southern England, they have severely declined to a few surviving colonies in the southwest.

Lesser horseshoe bat
Rhinolophus hipposideros
This species is much smaller than the greater horseshoe bat, with a wingspan of 23-24 cm. They are more widespread in southwest England, Wales and western Ireland, but nevertheless remain one of the scarcer species.

──── PLATE 2 ────

Long-eared bat and barbastelle

Brown long-eared bat (Long-eared bat of Thorburn)
Plecotus auritus
Since Thorburn's time it has been discovered that there are two species of long-eared bats in Britain. Only one, the brown long-eared bat, is widespread, in Britain and Ireland; the other, the grey long-eared bat, *Plecotus austriacus*, is found only in a few localities on the south coast of England. The extraordinary ears make the long-eared bats easily recognised. This is a small bat, with wingspan of about 24-28 cm. Flight is slow and fluttering, with much hovering around trees to pick insects off the foliage, although most food is caught in flight as in other bats.

They roost mainly in attics in summer, sometimes in tree-holes, and often in caves in winter. Like other bats that roost in roof-spaces they are vulnerable to poisoning by chemicals used for wood preservation. All bats are protected by UK law and it is mandatory to report a colony to the statutory conservation authority before undertaking any action that will harm them.

Barbastelle
Barbastella barbastellus
This is one of the rarest and most elusive of bats in Britain, and one of the least known. As in the long-eared bats, the ears meet on the forehead, but they are more normal in size. The overall colour is very dark. Barbastelles are limited to England and Wales, mostly in the south and east. They are usually associated with woodland, and roost in buildings and tree-holes in summer, sometimes in caves in winter.

──── PLATE 3 ────

Pipistrelle and noctule

Pipistrelle
Pipistrellus pipistrellus
This is by far the most widespread and abundant bat in Britain and Ireland, and one of the smallest, with a wingspan of about 20-24 cm. However analysis of their ultrasounds has suggested that two separate species might be involved and this has been supported by biochemical studies. The relative abundance and distribution of these are as yet unknown.

In summer females form large nursery colonies. These are usually in houses, including modern ones, but hidden in crevices under tiles and behind wall cladding rather than in open attics. These sites are abandoned in late summer when the young have dispersed. Pipistrelles emerge from their daytime roost about half an hour after sunset and feed mainly on tiny flies. The young are born in late June or early July and fly at an age of three weeks.

Noctule
Nyctalus noctula (Vesperugo noctula of Thorburn*)*
This is the largest bat in Britain, with a wingspan of about 34-44 cm. The fur is a rich reddish brown all over, with the hairs uniformly coloured from tip to root. Noctules are widespread in England and Wales but absent from Ireland. They roost mainly in hollow trees and feed on large insects such as cockchafers and crickets. They fly high and fast around sunset, overlapping in activity with foraging swifts. The mothers sometimes move

home while suckling, carrying their infants (always singles) with them.

PLATE 4

Leisler's bat and serotine

Leisler's bat

Nyctalus leisleri (Vesperugo leisleri of Thorburn*)*
Leisler's bat is a smaller relative of the noctule, with a wingspan of about 29-33 cm. The fur is less reddish, and the hairs are two-coloured, with dark bases, seen by blowing the fur, and pale tips. They are much less common in Britain, mainly in SE England and the Midlands, but are widespread in Ireland. They are woodland bats, roosting mainly in tree-holes, sometimes in buildings. Although generally a scarce species, they have used artificial bat-boxes.

Serotine

Eptesicus serotinus (Veperugo serotinus of Thorburn*)*
The serotine is a large bat with especially broad wings and a wingspan of about 33-37 cm. The upper surface is less reddish than in the noctule and the underside is distinctly paler. It is almost confined to south and southeastern England, mainly from Suffolk to Dorset.

Serotines roost mainly in older buildings, usually forming small breeding colonies and often unobtrusively tucked into crevices. They emerge early in the evening and feed especially around trees, having a much slower flight than the noctules. The prey consists mostly of larger beetles and moths which are caught and eaten on the wing. Most young are born in July and fly at an age of 4-5 weeks.

PLATE 5

Natterer's and Daubenton's bats

These bats belong to the genus *Myotis* which can be distinguished by the elongate, pointed 'tragus' in the ear, well seen in the painting of Natterer's. This is a fleshy lobe involved with the reception of echo-location signals, found in all British bats other than the horseshoe bats. In the preceding four species the tragus is short and rounded.

Natterer's bat

Myotis nattereri
A small greyish brown bat, almost white below, with pale face and membranes, and a fringe of stiff hairs along the margin of the tail membrane. The wingspan is about 26-29 cm. They are wide-spread in Britain and Ireland. In summer the females form nursery colonies of up to 200 in buildings. In winter hibernation is usually in caves, tunnels or old mine workings. They emerge to feed well after sunset and hunt especially around trees. Bat-boxes set in conifer plantations, which are short of natural crevices and holes, have been successful in attracting this species.

Daubenton's bat

Myotis daubentonii
This is similar to Natterer's bat, with pale underside and pinkish face, but the feet are very large and the tail membrane lacks a conspicuous fringe. It is equally widespread in Britain and Ireland. In summer they form nursery colonies in hollow trees, buildings and sometimes under bridges. They feed especially over water, skimming close to the surface to catch caddis flies and other insects. In winter they live mainly in caves, sometimes in crevices under scree.

PLATE 6

Whiskered and Bechstein's bats

Since Thorburn's time it has been discovered that the whiskered bat, as then known, really comprises two distinct species, now known as the whiskered bat (*Myotis mystacinus*) and Brandt's bat (*Myotis brandti*). The latter is more reddish brown and is widespread in England and Wales.

Whiskered bat

Myotis mystacinus
This is a small bat, with a wingspan of about 22-23 cm. It is distinguished from the other *Myotis* bats, except Brandt's, by the very dark skin of the face and membranes, although the fur is also a rather dark greyish brown above and lighter, but still dusky, below. They are widespread in England, Wales and Ireland, but only in southern Scotland.

Summer colonies are commonly in buildings, often under the ridge tiles; in winter they are found mainly in caves and cellars. They can be very inconspicuous as they cling to the walls of a cave, blending with the grey rock, although sometimes noticeable by the sparkle of dew-drops on the fur.

Bechstein's bat

Myotis bechsteinii
This is one of the rarest bats in Britain, being confined to a triangle from the Isle of Wight to Gloucester and Somerset, and even there usually found rarely as single individuals in tree-holes. The ears are noticably long, but still only about two-thirds the length of those of the long-eared bats. Very little is known about its habits.

—————— PLATE 7 ——————

Hedgehog
Erinaceus europaeus

Hedgehogs are found throughout Britain and Ireland in a variety of habitats. Ideally they like thick undergrowth to provide secluded nesting sites, adjacent to grassland where they can forage. Woodland and hedgerows are suitable, but gardens, parks and golf courses are also favoured provided they are not over-tidied. Hedgehogs prey on a wide variety of invertebrate animals, especially beetles, caterpillars, earthworms and slugs.

The hedgehog is one of our few hibernating species, apart from the bats. Hibernation lasts from October or November to April, when the body temperature remains at about 4°C and the heart-beat falls from about 190 to about 20 per minute. However they usually awaken once or twice during the winter and may even move to another nest.

Breeding takes place in spring when usually 4-6 young are born. They are weaned at about 4-6 weeks. A second litter is sometimes produced but these later youngsters often have difficulty in laying up enough fat to survive the winter.

The formidable spines of hedgehogs protect them from most predators but badgers in particular have the knack of prizing them open. Their habit of rolling into a ball is no protection against motor traffic and large numbers perish on the roads.

—————— PLATE 8 ——————

Mole
Talpa europaea

Moles live almost their entire lives underground; any seen on the surface are likely to be young animals dispersing from their parental home. They are widespread in Britain (but not in Ireland) and occur at altitudes up to 1000 metres if there is enough depth of soil. The characteristic 'mole-hills' of soil are especially noticeable on pasture but they also occur in woodland and on stabilized sandy soils on the coast. Moles have very tiny but functional eyes concealed in the fur, and no external ears although their hearing is acute.

Each animal lives in a tunnel excavated with the spade-like front feet. Each tunnel system has one nest, sometimes identified by a larger heap on the surface. In spring the males extend their tunnels to intercept those of females. A litter of three or four young is born in spring, sometimes followed by a second. During dispersal the youngsters often come to the surface and are then sometimes taken by owls and buzzards.

Moles feed entirely on invertebrate animals, especially earthworms but also the larvae of beetles (e.g. wireworms, the larvae of click-beetles) and flies (e.g. leather jackets, the larvae of craneflies). Worms are often stored after being paralysed by a bite in the head.

Moles are a nuisance on bowling and golf greens, but otherwise do little harm and most farmers no longer consider them worth controlling.

—————— PLATE 9 ——————

Shrews

Although superficially mouse-like, shrews are more closely related to the hedgehogs and moles in the order Insectivora. They have slender snouts with continuous rows of pointed teeth, well adapted to feeding on insects and other small invertebrates. They tend to be hyperactive little animals with several periods of intense activity alternating with shorter periods of rest throughout day and night. Only three species occur on the British mainland but two additional species of white-toothed shrews, genus Crocidura, occur on the Channel and Scilly islands.

Common shrew
Sorex araneus

Common shrews occur throughout Britain (but not Ireland) in many different habitats: woodland, hedgerows, long grass, moorland, dunes and the less tidy parks and gardens. They make shallow burrows or surface runs, and also use those of rodents. They start breeding in the spring following their birth and produce two or three litters of about six young before dying in the autumn.

Pygmy shrew
Sorex minutus

Pygmy shrews differ from common shrews in their smaller size (head and body about 4-5 cm, against 5-8 cm in the common shrew), and relatively longer and thicker tail. They live at ground level, burrowing through moss and grass. They are even more widespread than the common shrew, reaching many of

the offshore islands, and tend to replace the common shrew at higher altitudes.

Water shrew
Neomys fodiens
Water shrews are a little larger than common shrews and much darker, almost black, above. Fringes of silvery hairs on the tail and hind feet make them competent swimmers. They find much of their food underwater in the form of crustaceans and other invertebrates as well as small fish, killed by a venomous bite. Water shrews are widespread but sparse throughout Britain, but not Ireland, mostly but not entirely near fresh water.

— PLATE 10 —

Wild cat
Felis silvestris (Felis catus of Thorburn*)*
The Scottish wild cat (for it is long since extinct in the rest of the British Isles) is a remnant of a once widespread species of cat extending from central Europe to Africa and including the ancestor of our domestic cats. Wild cats are widespread in the Scottish Highlands, mainly in woodland. The more pure-bred individuals have dark stripes (not blotches) on the body, and the tail is thick, blunt-ended, and with clear dark bands. However some hybridization with domestic cats takes place and it is unlikely that pure wild cats could ever recolonise the lowlands because they would be genetically swamped by feral cats of domestic origin.

Wild cats are elusive and mainly nocturnal. They prey mainly on rodents, rabbits and birds. One litter of usually 3-5 kittens is produced in May in a den under rocks or tree roots; later breeding probably indicates the influence of domestic cats.

Thorburn depicted the traditional sportsman's view of a cornered cat snarling at a gun. Wild cats are no larger than big domestic cats, and feral domestic cats are widespread and abundant throughout the country wherever there is human habitation. Like their domestic relatives wild cats are efficient predators but their reputation for size and ferocity has been greatly exaggerated.

— PLATE 11 —

Fox
Vulpes vulpes (Canis vulpes of Thorburn*)*
Foxes are almost ubiquitous throughout the British Isles from city centres to the mountain tops, although some of the greater densities occur in suburban areas. They are territorial animals with a complex social organization that varies considerably according to habitat and population density. Typically there is one male with several females of which only one will breed, with younger females sometimes helping to rear the cubs. There may be up to five such groups per square kilometre in some urban areas; typically about one per square kilometre in rural areas; and as little as one per 40 square kilometres in some Scottish hill country.

Foxes usually excavate a den to have their cubs, but at other times often lie up for the day above ground. Mating takes place in January when much barking takes place. Cubs are usually born in March, often 3-5 in a litter.

Foxes are adaptable predators, but rabbits, voles, rats and mice are the most frequent victims. They frequently eat earthworms, and scavenge on carrion and human refuse when the opportunity occurs. They can of course cause trouble amongst unprotected poultry and reared pheasants; however there is a growing appreciation that traditional hunting by hounds is neither an efficient nor a humane method of control, and indeed in most situations any kind of control is quite unnecessary.

— PLATE 12 —

Walrus
Odobenus rosmarus (Trichechus rosmarus of Thorburn*)*
The walrus is the most distinctive member of the Pinnipedia, a group that includes the seals and sealions, and one of the largest, adult males reaching about 3.5 metres in length and about 850 kg in weight. The tusks, enlarged upper canine teeth, are unique and are present in both sexes, although smaller in females. The forward-directed hind feet, which can be used on land, relate it to the sealions rather than the seals in which the hind feet cannot be turned forward and are used only for swimming.

The walrus is an Arctic species, living amongst the pack-ice wherever the water is shallow enough (up to 75 metres) to allow them to feed on the bottom. They prey mainly on clams. Walruses live in herds. The young are born in May on the ice and remain with their mothers for about two years.

Walruses have always been hunted by indigenous people of the Arctic and provided a great range of products from meat to hide, used to make boats. The intestines provided the traditional Eskimo parkas. Commercial exploitation wiped out many populations and there are now very few in the Atlantic sector (Greenland, Spitzbergen etc.) but more in the Pacific sector, around the Bering Straits. They sometimes wander south and there are about forty records of vagrants in British waters, mainly around the Orkney and Shetland islands.

PLATE 13

Grey seal
Halichoerus grypus
Grey seals are confined to the North Atlantic with almost half of the total population around Britain and Ireland. This is the larger of the two resident seals in British waters, with males about 2 metres long and weighing up to 300 kg. Colour and pattern are very variable but the chief distinguishing features are in the head: in adults the profile between the crown and the nose is straight or convex and the muzzle is longer than in the common seal.

Grey seals live round most of the British and Irish coast, but are scarce in the English Channel. They feed on many kinds of fish, sand-eels and cod often predominating. In autumn they come ashore to breed, mainly on rocky coasts and islands, with the biggest concentrations in the Outer Hebrides and the Orkneys.

The pups have a white coat and remain on land for about three weeks, growing rapidly on a diet of milk with a fat content of 55 per cent. At the end of lactation mating takes place before they return to the sea, both sexes having fasted throughout the breeding season.

Females start breeding at an age of about 3-5 years, males at about 6. Males have been recorded up to 26 years of age and one female is known to have reached 46.

PLATE 14

Common seal
Phoca vitulina
The common seal, also known as the harbour seal, is smaller than the grey seal, up to about 1.5 metres in length and 130 kg in weight. In profile the forehead is concave and the muzzle is noticeably shorter than in the grey seal. Like the grey seal these seals are widespread around Britain and Ireland. They prefer less exposed coasts and are the commoner species in estuaries and sandy bays.

They can be seen 'hauled-out' on sand banks when they often adopt a characteristic 'banana' posture, with head and tail in the air. On more exposed coasts these hauled-out groups often comprise both species. The biggest concentrations in Britain are in the Wash, Orkneys, Shetland and the Inner Hebrides. They feed on a wide variety of fish and also take shrimps and cuttlefish.

Breeding behaviour is quite different from that of the grey seal. A single pup is born in June or July on sandy beaches or sandbanks, or even in the water. They are born with an adult-coloured coat and can swim immediately. They are suckled in the water so that they do not have to remain ashore like pups of grey seals.

PLATE 15

Ringed seal and harp seal
These are both Arctic seals that only occasionally wander south to British waters.

Ringed seal

Phoca hispida
This is a close relative of the common seal from which it differs in having the dark spots on the body surrounded by paler rings, hence the name. However the difference is not conspicuous and it is possible that many ringed seals that stray south remain undetected amongst the common seals. Ringed seals live all around the Arctic Ocean. They spend much of their time under the ice, especially in winter, keeping small breathing holes open, even in ice up to two metres thick. Breeding takes place in spring, without the formation of large colonies. The single pup is usually born in a den excavated in snow on the ice. The pups have white coats and are suckled for about two months.

Although they do not undergo migrations, some individuals wander south and about a dozen have been detected in British waters.

Harp seal
Phoca groenlandica
Adult male harp seals are easily recognized by the prominent pattern as illustrated, but in females the dark areas are less prominent and partly obscured by spotting, while immatures are more heavily spotted. They are only a little larger than common seals. Although they live round the edge of the Arctic ice they are more gregarious than the ringed seals and distinctly migratory, moving south in autumn and winter to stay in open water.

Breeding takes place on ice in the spring, when they form large colonies. The pups have a silky white coat and have been

heavily exploited for the fur trade.

Because of their migratory habits harp seals stray into British waters more frequently than do ringed seals but nevertheless are only rare vagrants.

—— PLATE 16 ——

Bearded and hooded seals

These are two further species of Arctic seals that are only rare vagrants in British waters, usually in the northern isles.

Bearded seal

Erignathus barbatus

This is a large seal, up to about 2.3 metres long, with a rather small head and very prominent whiskers, reminiscent of a walrus. The colour is a rather uniform greyish brown, without spots. Bearded seals live around the Arctic ice wherever there is shallow water, for they feed mainly on animals found on the sea-bed, including crabs, clams, octopus and flatfish. They breed on the ice, without forming large colonies, pups being born mostly in April.

They are not migratory but occasionally stray south as far as Orkney and Shetland.

Hooded seal

Cystophora cristata

The name refers to the extraordinary inflatable hood on the nose of the adult male. The illustration shows this only slightly inflated — when fully inflated it can be considerably larger than a football, and on top of that the seal is able to inflate a red balloon from one nostril. This is a large, rather solitary seal, up to 2.5 metres long in adult males. Females or young could easily be confused with grey seals.

Hooded seals occur in the Atlantic sector of the Arctic, usually amongst drifting ice-floes in deep water. The pups are born in May with a beautiful silvery bluish grey coat which has led to heavy exploitation in the past. Only occasional stragglers reach British waters.

—— PLATE 17 ——

Otter

Lutra lutra (Lutra vulgaris of Thorburn)

Otters are amongst the largest and most specialized members of the weasel family (Mustelidae). They are highly adapted for an aquatic life, with powerful, tapering tails, webbed feet and sleek, water-repellent fur covering dense, insulating under-fur. They are very agile under water where they catch most of their prey.

Otters were once found throughout the British Isles in fresh water as well as on many parts of the coast. By the 1960s they had become extinct or greatly depleted in many lowland areas, primarily through poisoning by pesticides, although exacerbated by persecution, insensitive drainage and increased disturbance. Now legally protected, they have begun to recover in most areas, although increasing road traffic takes a toll.

Otters prey upon many different fish, but eels often predominate. Coastal otters in Scotland also feed predominantly on fish, but crabs also make up a significant part of the diet. Otters use dens — 'holts'— which are often in cavities under trees or rocks. Breeding is not highly seasonal although most births are in summer. The young, usually two or three, begin to leave the holt at an age of about seven weeks. They take about two years to mature.

Except in areas remote from human activity otters are usually active only at night and are consequently difficult to see. Their presence can usually be detected by the characteristic droppings or 'spraints' that serve to mark their territories. These are deposited on prominent stones, logs etc, have a distinctive musky odour and consist largely of bones and scales of fish.

—— PLATE 18 ——

Badger

Meles meles (Meles taxus of Thorburn)

Although members of the weasel family, badgers are much more heavily built than other mustelids. The very distinctive black and white striped head means that they are firmly implanted in public imagination in spite of the fact that they are rarely seen. Badgers live in small social groups each in a system of tunnels, a 'sett', usually excavated in woodland or in a hedgerow bank. Setts commonly have up to ten entrances of which three or four will be in use at any one time. The total length of tunnel may be well over a hundred metres and it is likely that some setts are hundreds of years old. Active holes usually have recently excavated soil on the spoil-heap outside, often accompanied by discarded bedding in the form of grass or bracken.

Badgers forage at night, often on grassland where earthworms are the principal prey, although they are versatile feeders and will take bulbs, vole nestlings, beetles, fruit, acorns, fungi and much more. They generally mate in spring but development of the embryo does not begin until about December. The young, often three or four, are usually born in February and emerge for their first outing in April.

Badgers are very widespread in Britain and Ireland. Although commonly persecuted in the past in the interests of game preservation and in the 'sport' of badger baiting with dogs, they are now legally protected and thriving in most parts of the country.

—— PLATE 19 ——

Pine marten

Martes martes (Mustela martes of Thorburn)

The pine marten is one of a group of species, including the sable, that replace each other around the world in the northern temperate forests. They are large, agile members of the weasel family, as much at home in the tree-tops as on the ground. By the early 20th century persecution by game-keepers had reduced the pine marten to a small remnant in the northern highlands of Scotland and brought them close to extinction in Wales and England. Relaxation of keepering, along with reafforestation and, latterly, legal protection have allowed the population to expand. Martens are now widespread in the Highlands and survive, albeit still sparsely, in Wales, northern England and southwestern Scotland. They are also widespread but sparse throughout Ireland.

Martens are versatile predators. Field voles and rabbits are often the dominant prey, but they frequently take birds and insects, especially beetles, and take full advantage of the autumn glut of berries. Although often reported to prey upon squirrels, this is probably unusual — squirrels can match the agility of martens, and other prey is usually much easier to catch.

Mating takes place in July or August and, as with most mustelids, development of the embryos is delayed so that birth takes place in spring, usually a single litter of two to four. They are born in a nest which may be amongst rocks, under a fallen tree, or above ground in a tree-hole, squirrel nest or, quite often, in the attic of a house or outbuilding.

—— PLATE 20 ——

Polecat

Mustela putorius

The polecat is more familiar to most people in its domesticated, usually albino form, the ferret. The sleek dark outer hair of a wild polecat scarcely conceals the paler underfur, sometimes producing a transient mottled effect as seen in the illustration. The facial pattern is very characteristic, but is also seen, usually in a dilute form, in some dark varieties of ferret, known as polecat-ferrets.

Once widespread in Britain (but not in Ireland) polecats were exterminated from the whole country except central Wales by the early 20th century. They have subsequently recovered and extended their range throughout Wales and into many adjacent parts of England. Feral ferrets occur elsewhere, with a long-established population on Mull and on some other islands.

Polecats live and hunt at ground level, in both woodland and open country, including marshland. Rabbits are usually the principal prey, followed by rodents, birds and frogs. They breed in spring, without any delay between mating and development of the embryos. The den is most often in a commandeered rabbit burrow where a single litter of around five to seven kits are born about June. Polecats are renowned for the powerful scent produced by glands at the base of the tail. This is used, as in other members of the family, to mark their territory, but is obnoxious enough to deter predators. However polecats cannot eject the scent as a missile as the American skunks do.

Stoat

Mustela erminea

Stoats are the most familiar members of the weasel family since they are active by day and frequently seen as they cross roads or run along roadside verges. They are distinguished from

weasels by the prominent black tip to the tail. The stoat is one of two species in Britain to turn more or less white in winter, the other being the mountain hare. Stoats are widespread in Britain and Ireland, in any habitat with a modicum of cover — roadside verges, crops, woodland, and to the tops of the highest hills amongst scree.

In Ireland, where weasels are absent, stoats tend to be a little smaller than in Britain and the pale underside is normally narrower, with a more irregular line separating it from the brown flanks. The pure white winter coat — 'ermine' — (the tail-tip always remains black) is usually achieved in the north of Scotland; further south various degrees of partial whitening occur, depending mainly upon the temperature in autumn when the moult takes place. Male stoats are substantially larger than females — head and body lengths are about 30 and 26 cm respectively.

Stoats are active predators, hunting mainly on the ground for rabbits and small rodents, but they are also agile climbers and birds and eggs form a significant part of the diet. Stoats are often seen to 'dance', frantically dashing to and fro and leaping about, perhaps in an attempt to mesmerise prey, although it has been suggested that it is connected with a common infestation by a roundworm that penetrates the brain.

Stoats mate in summer, but development is delayed until the following spring, with birth of a single litter of about six to ten young in April or May.

PLATE 23

Weasel

Mustela nivalis (Mustela vulgaris of Thorburn*)*
The weasel is the smallest of the carnivores, smaller than the stoat and distinguished by the shorter, uniformly coloured tail. They are widespread in Britain but absent from Ireland. Like the stoat they are found in many different habitats but because of the small size and ability to travel in mouse and vole tunnels they are less often seen. As with the stoat, males are larger than females; length of the head and body is usually about 20-21 cm in males and 17-18 cm in females. However some females start breeding before they are fully grown, and this has led to a belief that there is a separate small species although this is almost certainly not the case.

Weasels are small enough to hunt mice and voles in their burrows and runways and these always dominate the diet. Males also tackle small rabbits and both sexes take birds, both on the ground and in bushes and trees, entering nest-boxes and natural tree-holes with ease. Weasels do not show any delay between mating and development of the young. They breed in spring, producing one or two litters of four to six young.

PLATE 24

Red squirrel (Common squirrel of Thorburn)
Sciurus vulgaris
Since Thorburn wrote around 1920 the range of the native red squirrel has contracted substantially as it has been replaced by the introduced American grey squirrel. In England red squirrels are now confined to the extreme north, with isolated populations in the Isle of Wight, Norfolk and Staffordshire. They remain more widespread in Wales, Scotland and Ireland. Thorburn's plate shows the red squirrel in winter coat when it is much greyer than in summer and has very distinctive tufts on the ears. However there is considerable variation in colour because of introduction of animals from the continent where many colour varieties occur.

Red squirrels live predominantly in woodland containing coniferous trees, and in pure coniferous plantations they appear to be safe from competition by the greys. In mixed or wholly broad-leaved woods grey squirrels generally replace the reds, probably by competing more successfully for food when it is at its scarcest in late winter.

Red squirrels feed predominantly upon tree seeds, especially those of conifers such as pines which they obtain by stripping the scales off the cone with their incisor teeth, leaving a characteristic core. However they also take other seeds and nuts, buds, bark, fungi and caterpillars. The nest or 'drey' is a sphere of twigs and leaves usually in a fork close to the trunk of a tree. A litter of about three young is born any time between February and August.

PLATE 25

Common dormouse
Muscardinus avellanarius
This is the only dormouse that is native to Britain, although the much larger and greyer fat dormouse has been introduced in southeastern England. The common dormouse is widespread in suitable habitat in southern England and Wales, with two or three outlying populations in northern England. They are absent from Scotland and Ireland. Both dormice are distinguished from other mice by their bushy tails.

Compared with other small rodents, dormice have rather specialized requirements; they need broad-leaved woodland with a good shrub layer and a variety of tree species, including those with edible seed such as hazel, sweet chestnut and beech. Dormice are active only at night when they forage with great agility in the tree-tops and shrubs, rarely coming to the ground. They feed on buds and flowers in spring and summer, on seeds, nuts and fruit in autumn. They are adept at gnawing

During the summer harvest mice live largely above ground, making small spherical nests that are anchored to grass stems, and they climb with great agility amongst the grass and tall herbs. In winter they nest in grass tussocks at ground level but remain active. They feed mainly on seeds but also take insects. The young are born in the summer nest, usually several litters of four to six each summer.

Wood mouse
Apodemus sylvaticus (Mus sylvaticus of Thorburn*)*
The wood mouse is the most abundant and ubiquitous mouse in Britain and Ireland. Although primarily a woodland animal it is versatile, living abundantly in gardens, parks, hedgerows and crops, and coming into houses in autumn. Woodmice are agile climbers but spend much of their time on the ground, feeding principally on seeds but also on buds and insects. They are prolific, producing several litters of four to seven young through the summer and sometimes even in mild winters.

They occur on many islands where they are often larger than on the mainland. The 'St Kilda wood mouse' shown in plate 27 is one such island race.

open hazel nuts, leaving a neat hole with smooth edges quite different from those opened by other rodents and therefore providing a useful way of detecting the presence of these very elusive animals.

Dormice are unique amongst British rodents in hibernating. The winter is spent in deep sleep in a nest that is usually at or below ground level. Hibernation usually lasts from October to April. In summer they nest above ground in a tree-hole or in thick shrubs. They are less prolific than other rodents, producing only one or two litters per year, each of about four young. The young remain in the nest for about a month and stay with the mother for a further month or two, not breeding until the following summer.

─────────── PLATE 26 ───────────

Harvest mouse and wood mouse
These two mice belong to the family Muridae which also includes the rats.

Harvest mouse
Micromys minutus (Mus minutus of Thorburn*)*
This is the smallest British mouse, with the length of head and body only about 5-7 cm. The ears are very short and the long slender tail can be used as a support by twining it around stems as shown in the plate. Harvest mice are widely distributed in most of England but are scarce in the north and in Wales, with one or two outlying populations in southern Scotland and none in Ireland.

Although traditionally depicted in cereal fields, modern farming methods are not sympathetic to harvest mice and they are now found mainly in what is presumably their original habitat, namely long grass. This may be on road verges, especially adjacent to hedgerows, and amongst the tall grasses and herbs that grow in wet habitats such as marshes and on the edges of ponds and slow rivers.

─────────── PLATE 27 ───────────

Yellow-necked mouse and St Kilda wood mouse
The St Kilda wood mouse is a subspecies of the wood mouse, *Apodemus sylvaticus*, dealt with on Plate 26. Although Thorburn treated the yellow-necked mouse also as a subspecies of the wood mouse, it had, even before he wrote, been recognised as a distinct species, albeit closely related to the wood mouse.

Yellow-necked mouse (Yellow-necked wood mouse of Thorburn)
Apodemus flavicollis (Mus sylvaticus wintoni of Thorburn*)*
This mouse is very similar to the wood mouse but nevertheless differs in a number of ways: the fur of the upper surface is a richer colour, the underside is a lighter grey and it is a little larg-

er. The most distinctive feature is the yellow collar. Whereas the wood mouse has (usually) a narrow yellowish streak in the centre of the chest, in the yellow-necked mouse this is expanded sideways in a broad band.

Yellow-necked mice are confined to southern England and much of Wales, and even there have a rather patchy distribution. They are associated especially with mature, broad-leaved woodland and are perhaps even more arboreal than the wood mice, although their habits, feeding and breeding are very similar. Like the wood mice they frequently enter houses, especially in lofts where fruit is stored.

PLATE 28

House mouse (Common mouse and St Kilda house mouse of Thorburn)
Mus musculus
The house mouse was probably originally a native of the grasslands of western Asia but it adapted to living in and around human dwellings from an early period and has been in Britain at least since the Iron Age, for over 2000 years. It differs from the wood mouse mainly in having shorter ears and smaller eyes, and in lacking the sharp contrast between dark upper and pale under side, the overall colour being much greyer than in the other mice.

House mice occur in all kinds of buildings, but especially in farmyards where grain is abundant. They frequently live outdoors in arable fields and adjacent hedges and ditches, but rarely in woodland or other more natural habitats. Like the other mice they are predominantly nocturnal. Although principally seed-eaters they are very versatile in their feeding habits, taking all kinds of stored food and also insects. House mice are notoriously prolific and can breed all year in heated buildings, producing litters of usually five to eight young throughout the year.

House mice are widespread on small islands where they can sometimes survive away from human habitats if competitors are absent. The race on the main island of St Kilda, west of the Outer Hebrides, was especially large, and rather pale below, but became extinct when the island was evacuated in 1930, probably due to competition from the wood mouse which still survives there.

PLATE 29

Ship rat (Black rat and Alexandrine rat of Thorburn)
Rattus rattus
Like the house mouse this rat has become worldwide in association with man, although it is less common in the cooler temperate regions. Often called the black rat, it occurs in a variety of colour forms, although the ones that were formerly widespread in European ports were predominantly black. The 'Alexandrine rat' is a colour form of the same species with brown upper parts and grey belly, and is the dominant form in many tropical areas. Both forms are distinguished from the more widespread common rat by their larger ears and longer, thinner tail.

Ship rats were once the dominant rats in towns throughout Britain and Ireland, at least from Roman times, but were largely displaced by the common rat in the 18th and 19th centuries. They are now almost extinct in Britain, perhaps surviving in small numbers in some ports, and also on some small islands including Lundy in the Bristol Channel, the Shiant Islands in the Hebrides and Inchcolm in the Firth of Forth.

Ship rats are descended from arboreal ancestors and are agile climbers that were more often found in the upper storeys of buildings than common rats. Like other rats they are predominantly grain-eaters but are very adaptable.

PLATE 30

Common rat (Brown rat of Thorburn)
Rattus norvegicus (Mus decumanus of Thorburn*)*
This rat is another worldwide associate of man but tends to be more predominant than the ship rat in temperate regions. It is a slightly larger animal, with head and body up to 28 cm but usually less; the ears are less prominent and the tail thicker and shorter than that of the ship rat. Although the colour is usually brown above and grey below, black individuals sometimes occur.

This is now the common, widespread rat in Britain and Ireland. Although improved packaging and containerisation of goods in transit and in warehouses have helped to reduce numbers, they are still common, especially on arable farms. They are competent swimmers and often live on river banks where they could be mistaken for water voles. Although principally seed-eaters, rats owe their success to their versatility and they can feed on root-crops, meat, fish and even soap and candles. They often forage on the seashore, feeding on carrion and other debris on the tide-line.

Rats are serious pests by reason of their depredations on stored food and transmission of disease, but they have an undeserved reputation for size and ferocity in the public mind. Although well able to inflict a serious bite when handled, they are

not aggressive. Breeding may continue throughout the year if food is abundant, as on refuse tips, or may be confined to summer. Litter size is very variable, but is commonly six to nine.

PLATE 31

Bank vole, Field vole and Orkney vole

These three mouse-sized voles are distinguished from the true mice by their shorter tails, ears and hind feet, blunter snouts, smaller eyes and longer fur. They also differ in their more completely vegetarian diet.

Bank vole

Clethrionomys glareolus (Evotomys glareolus of Thorburn)
Bank voles are characterised by the distinctly reddish brown fur on the back, and a tail about half the length of the head and body. They are widespread in Britain, but in Ireland are confined to the southwest. They live in woodland with thick undergrowth, and in hedgerows and gardens, but avoid open grassland.

They feed mainly on leaves (for example of bramble), buds and seeds, but also take some insects. Breeding takes place from spring to autumn, with several litters of about four young.

Field vole

Microtus agrestis
Field voles have even shorter tails and ears than bank voles and the fur is a greyish brown above. They feed mainly on grasses and sedges. They occur throughout Britain (but not Ireland) wherever there is moderately long grass, including moorland, dunes, field margins and road verges.

They are preyed upon by owls, as well as by kestrels, buzzards and all the predatory mammals. Numbers fluctuate greatly from year to year, usually with a four-year cycle of abundance and scarcity.

Orkney vole

Microtus arvalis (Microtus orcadensis of Thorburn)
The Orkney vole is very similar in appearance and life-style to the field vole. However it belongs to a species that is widespread in continental Europe but absent from the British

mainland. It was almost certainly introduced to the Orkney Islands at the time of the Neolithic settlement since its skeletal remains are abundant at archaeological sites dating back to about 3400 BC.

PLATE 32

Water vole

Arvicola terrestris (Arvicola amphibius of Thorburn)
The water vole is very similar in many respects to the field vole except for its much larger size (head and body about 12-25 cm), longer tail (about 60 per cent of head and body) and its aquatic habits. They are often mistaken for rats but the shorter muzzle, ears and tail all serve to distinguish them. Brown individuals are normal in most of the country but in northern Scotland the black form shown in the plate predominates. Both forms have been recorded in the same litter.

Water voles are widespread in Britain, but not in Ireland, wherever there is still or slow-flowing water with well vegetated banks. Like the other voles they are predominantly herbivorous, feeding especially on the succulent bases of grasses, sedges and other waterside herbs. They make burrows in river banks but also travel in runways amongst wetland vegetation. They are more active by day than rats and can often be seen swimming on quiet waters, diving with a plop when disturbed. In summer water voles are territorial, each occupying a stretch of river bank. They can have successive litters of about six young through the summer.

Water voles have declined considerably in recent years, possibly correlated with the expansion of the introduced feral American mink, although the two can coexist in favourable habitat.

PLATE 33

Brown hare (Common hare of Thorburn)
Lepus europaeus
Although often thought of as an indigenous species in Britain it is quite likely that the brown hare was introduced about Roman times. They are widespread throughout the lowlands of Britain but not in Ireland apart from a few very localised introductions. Brown hares are substantially larger than rabbits, with relatively longer ears and legs, and are further distinguished by the black tips to the ears and the black line on the upper surface of the tail.

Brown hares are especially associated with arable farmland. They do not burrow but rest by day crouching in a depression, becoming active especially at dusk and dawn. They feed on a variety of grasses and herbs, including young cereal crops. The 'boxing' behaviour seen especially in spring has always been difficult to interpret because the sexes are difficult to distinguish, but it usually appears to be a non-receptive female seeing off an over-amorous suitor. The young, usually two or three in a litter, are born above ground and are well developed at birth. They remain near their birthplace and are visited by their mother for a very brief but intense period of suckling each day, just after sunset.

Brown hares have declined considerably in recent decades in spite of relaxation of hunting in many areas. Modern farming practices do not provide the amount and diversity of suitable food that used to be available, and the use of chemical sprays is also likely to be especially damaging.

--------- PLATES 34 AND 35 ---------

Mountain hare and Irish hare
Lepus timidus
The mountain hare is a little smaller than the brown hare, with proportionately shorter ears and feet. The summer coat is greyish brown, duller than that of the brown hare. In Britain they are confined to high ground, being especially abundant on the moorlands of the eastern highlands of Scotland, but also present in southern Scotland and the Pennines. In Ireland, in the absence of brown hares, they are widespread at all altitudes.

In Britain, as elsewhere in its circumpolar range, they moult to a white winter coat, retaining only the black ear-tips (Plate 35). In Ireland they remain brown all year.

Mountain hares are often quite gregarious. In Scotland they feed mainly on heather, supplemented by sedges and grasses. As in other hares and rabbits most food passes through them twice. During the day they produce soft faeces which are eaten; at night the familiar hard, round pellets are produced. During spring and summer up to three litters are produced between March and July, sometimes earlier and later in Ireland. The usual litter size is two or three.

--------- PLATE 36 ---------

Rabbit
Oryctolagus cuniculus (Lepus cuniculus of Thorburn*)*
Rabbits are probably the best known of all British mammals, being both widespread, abundant and sufficiently active by day, especially at dusk and dawn, to attract attention. They originated in Spain and Portugal, but were introduced to Britain in the 11th century, as a domestic animal. They are now a serious agricultural pest. Although they were decimated by the introduction of the viral disease myxomatosis in the 1950s, they

have recovered substantially although still below their former numbers.

Rabbits differ from hares in being much more gregarious and in living in burrows. Warrens are often on the edge of a field or just inside a wood. They feed mainly on grasses but take many other plants including clovers and root crops. In winter especially, bark is stripped from trees, often preventing regeneration of woodland or the establishment of young plantations.

The reproductive potential of rabbits is legendary. Litters of three to seven can be produced from January to August, at monthly intervals. They may be born in a branch of the main burrow, but low-ranking mothers often excavate a separate short burrow away from the warren in which to give birth. As with the hares, the young are only visited briefly each day for suckling. They are small and blind at birth but begin to emerge from the burrow at about three weeks and can themselves breed at an age of about four months.

Rabbits are the principal prey of foxes, martens, polecats, buzzards and many other predators and would be much less of a problem if such predators were encouraged.

--------- PLATE 37 ---------

Red deer
Cervus elaphus
The red deer is the largest wild land mammal now living in Britain. It can be distinguished from its nearest relative, the introduced Japanese sika deer, *Cervus nippon*, by its larger size, unspotted adult coat and, in mature stags, by the presence of a second, forward-projecting tine on each antler immediately above the lowest or 'brow-tine'. Truly wild red deer occur throughout the Highlands of Scotland, the Lake District,

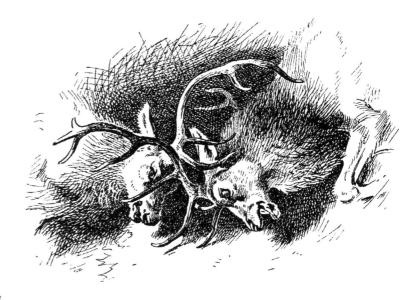

Exmoor and in East Anglia, but they are kept in parks and farms elsewhere and escapes are frequent. Although basically a woodland animal, in Scotland they spend most of the year on open hill country, descending to the valleys and into woodland in winter. They feed mainly on grasses, sedges and rushes in summer, but also browse trees and shrubs. In winter heather, bilberry and other shrubs are important.

For most of the year males (stags) and females (hinds) live in separate herds. During the mating season (rut) in autumn males compete by roaring and fighting and the dominant males attach themselves to groups of hinds. The antlers are shed in spring and regrown by the following autumn. Calves are born in May and June, usually singles.

The maintenance of red deer for hunting is a major land-use in the Scottish Highlands but the increasing numbers give cause for concern because of the damage to vegetation and the prevention of regeneration of woodland.

———————— PLATE 38 ————————

Fallow deer
Dama dama (Cervus dama of Thorburn*)*
The original range of fallow deer was around the Mediterranean. They were introduced to deer parks in Britain from the 11th century and have subsequently escaped to form feral populations in much of England and more locally in Wales, Scotland and Ireland. The plate depicts a mature buck with well developed antlers. In young bucks the characteristic flattening is much less obvious. The buck shows the typical spotted summer coat, but both uniformly light and uniformly dark individuals are frequent, as shown in the background, and all are unspotted or very faintly spotted in winter.

Fallow live in woodland or parkland and feed mainly on grass but also by browsing on trees and shrubs. They are gregarious deer, with a social organization and breeding system similar to those of the red deer. The bucks make deep groaning calls during the rut.

———————— PLATE 39 ————————

Roe deer
Capreolus capreolus
The roe deer is indigenous to Britain and is now widespread in Scotland, northern England, southern England and East Anglia, but absent from most of Wales and the Midlands (and from Ireland). They are smaller than the preceding species (about 60-70 cm high at the shoulder). The antlers (males only) are

much simpler, with usually three points in a mature buck, and are fully developed from about May to October. There is no visible tail. The summer coat is a rich reddish brown, as shown in the plate, with a small patch of white on the rump; in winter the coat is greyish brown and the white rump is more prominent.

Roe spend the day in woodland, usually alone or in pairs. They become most active at dusk and often emerge onto adjacent farmland. They feed by browsing, especially on bramble and on various deciduous trees and shrubs; also on ivy, bilberry and sometimes heather in winter.

In summer the bucks 'fray' saplings by scraping off strips of bark with their antlers to mark their territories. They mate in July and August but gestation is delayed until the following January, with birth in May or June, usually twins, sometimes one or three fawns.

———————— PLATES 40 AND 41 ————————

Park cattle (Wild white cattle of Thorburn)
Bos taurus
These plates depict cattle from three parkland herds, at Cadzow (Lanarkshire), Chartley (Staffordshire) and Chillingham (Northumberland). Only the last survives in a pure-bred condition. They are all characterised by white coat and spreading horns; the Chillingham breed has reddish ears, the others black ears. Much speculation has taken place as to the origin of these cattle. Truly wild cattle or aurochs, *Bos primigenius*, the ancestors of all domestic cattle, were present in Britain following the Ice Age but are likely to have been hunted to

extinction by about 1000 BC. It is unlikely that they were able to contribute to any domestic cattle, which are all likely to be derived from already domesticated stock imported from the continent.

Although there are historical references to feral white cattle in Medieval woodland, there is nothing to link these parkland herds with feral cattle rather than with Medieval domestic cattle that have survived little affected by the great diversification of breeds that took place by intensive selection, especially in the 18th century.

At present the Chillingham herd numbers about 50. They are kept under semi-natural conditions which allows their social organization and behaviour to be studied.

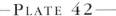

PLATE 42

Right and humpback whales
These are both 'baleen whales', the baleen being the filtering mechanism in the mouth that is used to strain crustaceans and small fish from the water. Baleen whales have no teeth, but instead a long series of flat horny plates with fringed edges hang from each upper jaw. Water is pushed out through the baleen by the tongue, leaving the food on the fringed inner edges.

Northern right whale
Eubalaena glacialis (Balaena australis of Thorburn)
The right whales were amongst the first to be hunted to near-extinction in the Atlantic. They once migrated in large numbers between wintering and breeding grounds in the Bay of Biscay to feed in summer in Arctic waters as far as Spitzbergen. They were hunted from shore-based whaling stations in the Outer Hebrides and Ireland, with 112 whales caught between 1908 and the 1920s. Now the total population in the North Atlantic numbers only a few hundred, mostly on the western side.

Right whales have no fin on the back and the baleen plates are very long, up to 2.5 metres.

Humpback whale
Megaptera novaeangliae (Megaptera boöps of Thorburn)
The plate, like most early representations of whales, gives a distorted impression of this species, which in life is much slimmer although not quite so stream-lined as the rorquals. The very long pale flippers are characteristic.

They migrate between waters off NW Africa in winter to around Iceland and Norway in summer. They are now very rare in the eastern North Atlantic but some are still occasionally seen off the western coasts of Scotland and Ireland.

Humpback whales are renowned for their 'songs' heard on the breeding ground and consisting of an extraordinary range of sound from coarse groans to pure wails.

PLATE 43

Rorquals
The rorquals are large, streamlined whales that are fast swimmers. They were all greatly over-exploited with the advent of steam whalers and explosive harpoons in the late 19th century. The grooves on the throat allow expansion and contraction of the mouth cavity during feeding.

Fin whale (Common rorqual of Thorburn)
Balaenoptera physalus (Balaenoptera musculus of Thorburn)
These are very large whales, about 20 metres in length. They are found in all oceans and were one of the principal species taken by the whaling industry both in the Antarctic and in the North Atlantic. There is still a regular migration off the west of Scotland and Ireland, with most sightings around the Outer Hebrides and Shetland, but usually well offshore. As in most migratory whales breeding takes place in the southern winter quarters, with one calf being born every two or three years.

Blue whale
Balaenoptera musculus (Balaenoptera sibbaldi of Thorburn)
The blue whale is the largest of all the whales and indeed the largest living animal, reaching 28 metres. It is a typical rorqual, with small flippers and very small back fin. At the time Thorburn wrote blue whales were still being caught off Shetland, the Outer Hebrides and Ireland. They are now very rare in the North Atlantic and especially in the eastern sector. They feed almost exclusively on small crustaceans. Like all the large whales they are potentially long-lived, to about 80 years, but do not begin to breed until they are over five, with a single youngster being produced at intervals of at least three years.

PLATE 44

Rorquals and bottle-nosed whale
Sei whale (Rudolphi's rorqual of Thorburn)
Balaenoptera borealis
This species is very similar to the fin whale but a little smaller, reaching about 14 metres. Like the other rorquals they migrate around the west of the British Isles between Iceland and sub-tropical seas. Sightings are now very rare and they are difficult to distinguish from fin whales at sea.

Minke whale (Lesser rorqual of Thorburn)
Balaenoptera acutorostrata
This is the smallest of the rorquals, reaching only about 8 metres. The white patch in the centre of each flipper is characteristic. They are still the most abundant of the baleen whales although they too have been greatly depleted by over-hunting. They are seen regularly around the islands of the Hebrides, Orkneys and Shetland and along the west coast of Ireland, and less regularly in the North and Irish Seas. They are less migratory than the larger whales and are more often seen from the shore. Minke whales feed mainly on shoals of fish such as herrings and sand-eels. The young are born in winter and are suckled for about six months.
(Bottle-nosed whale: see Plate 45.)

PLATE 45

Sperm whale and bottle-nosed whale
These and all the species in subsequent plates are toothed whales. They feed by catching prey — fish or squid — individually, rather than gulping shoals like the baleen whales.

Sperm whale
Physeter macrocephalus
The sperm whale is by far the largest of the toothed whales. There is a large discrepancy in size between the sexes, males reaching about 16 metres and females about 11 metres. The extraordinary head contains a large reservoir of fat — 'spermaceti' — which is believed to be involved in the control of buoyancy and perhaps in focusing sound. Male sperm whales migrate past the west of the British Isles from winter breeding quarters in the tropics to feed in northern waters. Females tend to remain in the south and are less often seen in British waters.

Sperm whales feed especially on squid and can dive to extreme depths — dives of well over a thousand metres have been recorded.

Bottle-nosed whale
Hyperoodon ampullatus (*Hyperoodon rostratum* of Thorburn) [*See also Plate 44*]
The bottle-nosed whale is the largest and best known of the 'beaked whales', reaching about 9 metres. These are toothed whales with only a single pair of teeth, in the lower jaw, in males only. They are deep-water whales, migrating around the west of the British Isles, with most sightings around the Outer Hebrides, Orkney and Shetland. Like the sperm whales they dive to great depths and feed mainly on squid. They were formerly taken in large numbers by Norwegian whalers and the population in European waters is still greatly depleted.

PLATE 46

Beaked whales (family *Ziphiidæ*)
Apart from the bottle-nosed whale (Plate 45) the beaked whales are elusive animals, widely distributed in the open oceans, but too dispersed and too fast to attract the attention of whalers. This is reflected in the English names, which are 'naturalists' names' rather than true vernacular names.

There is only one pair of teeth, in the lower jaws and only in males. They feed mainly on squid. Little is known about the details of their lives and most information comes from the occasional animal stranded on a beach.

Sowerby's beaked whale
Mesoplodon bidens
This whale, about 5 metres in length, is unusual in being found mostly in and around the North Sea, although there are some records also from the west coast. A few other species of Mesoplodon have been recorded very rarely on British coasts, usually through accidental stranding.

Cuvier's beaked whale
Ziphius cavirostris
This is one of the more distinctive of the beaked whales, with a pale head. The body usually bears numerous pale scars. These are found mostly in adult males and are believed to be caused by the teeth of rivals.

In British waters they are seen mostly around the Hebrides, usually singly but sometimes in small groups.

PLATE 47

White whale and narwhal
These are closely related, medium-sized whales, living all around the edge of the Arctic and only rarely wandering as far south as the British Isles.

White whale
Delphinapterus leucas
Adult white whales are pure white, while immature animals are grey or brown. They live mainly in shallow waters around the Arctic, feeding especially on squid but also on fish. They are very vocal, making a variety of bird-like whistles and chirps. There are a very few records of vagrants around the British Isles, mainly in northern Scotland.

Narwhal
Monodon monoceros
The narwhal must be one of the most bizarre of all animals. The

single spirally twisted tusk is really a tooth, normally developed only in males. The body length may reach about 4 metres, but tusks have been recorded up to 3 metres. Very rarely two tusks are present (the normal single one being a left tooth).

Narwhals occur throughout the Arctic Ocean and very rarely wander south as far as the British Isles. Although they have been seen to use the tusk to poke about on the seabed to disturb prey (they feed mainly on squid and bottom-living fish) the primary function of the tusks is presumably concerned with competition between adult males.

PLATE 48

Killer and pilot whales
These two species are amongst the larger members of the dolphin family, all of which have rows of numerous pointed teeth in both jaws. Those with the more pointed snouts tend to feed on fish, others on squid.

Killer whale
Orcinus orca (Orca gladiator of Thorburn)
Killer whales are unusual amongst the members of the dolphin family in showing a considerable difference between the sexes. Adult males are larger, reaching about 9.5 metres, against 5.5 metres of females.

In males also the centrally placed fin on the back becomes very tall, with both front and back margins straight; in females the fin is curved behind, as shown in the plate, and much shorter.

Killer whales live in small groups and are unusual in attacking other whales and seals, as well as feeding on fish, squid and birds. They are regular visitors off the west coast of Ireland and Scotland and around the northern isles, but also occur in the North Sea. Little is known about their breeding habits — births appear to take place far offshore in autumn and winter.

Pilot whale
Globicephala melas
Pilot whales are large dolphins, commonly up to 6 metres, lacking the narrow beak of some smaller species. These are sociable whales, often seen in groups of 20 to 40. It is one of the most easily seen species around the north and west of Scotland and the west of Ireland.

They feed mainly on squid, but also take fish. In the 19th century they were commonly caught in Shetland by driving herds into shallow bays until they grounded and this method has been used until recently in the Faeroe Islands.

PLATE 49

Porpoise and dolphins

Porpoise
Phocoena phocoena (Phocoena communis of Thorburn)
This is the only porpoise in European waters; in America it is called the harbour porpoise to distinguish it from other, Pacific, species. Porpoises differ from dolphins in their small size (up to 2 metres) and rounded snout, without a beak. The teeth are flattened rather than conical as in the dolphins. These are the most abundant and widespread of the cetaceans in British waters, living in shallow water and often entering estuaries. However they are difficult to detect unless the water is very calm, and their numbers have seriously declined in recent years.

Porpoises are usually seen in small groups. They feed mainly on fish but also take squid and crustaceans. The young are born (singly) in coastal waters in summer and suckle for about eight months.

Risso's dolphin (Risso's grampus of Thorburn)
Grampus griseus
This is a medium-sized dolphin (up to 3.5 metres) without a beak but with the typical tall, sickle-shaped fin of the dolphin family. They are regular in coastal waters around the west and north of the British Isles but rare in the North Sea. They feed mainly on squid. The body scars frequently seen on the adults are likely to be caused by sparring during the breeding season.

White-sided dolphin
Lagenorhynchus acutus
This is a typical, streamlined, fish-eating dolphin, up to 2.5 metres in length, with a distinctive pattern of white on the flanks. In British waters they are found mainly around the north and west of Scotland.

―――――PLATE 50―――――

Typical dolphins

White-beaked dolphin

Lagenorhynchus albirostris

A large dolphin, up to 2.7 metres, with a whitish beak and very long, pointed dorsal fin. This species is confined to the North Atlantic and is regular around the north and west of the British Isles, less frequent off North Sea coasts. They feed on fish.

Bottle-nosed dolphin

Tursiops truncatus (Tursiops tursio of Thorburn)

This is the best known dolphin in British waters and also the one that has been most often kept in dolphinaria. Thorburn's illustration is misleading since the body is usually a rather uniform grey, becoming lighter below but without any clear pattern. Bottle-nosed dolphins are resident around the north and west of Britain and in the northern North Sea. Easily visible groups live in the inner Moray Firth in NE Scotland and in Cardigan Bay in Wales. They live in small groups and feed mainly on fish. They sometimes leap clear of the water and also ride on the bow-waves of vessels.

Common dolphin

Delphinus delphis

Common dolphins are only common in waters to the south-west of the British Isles, although they occasionally stray further north. They are swift, streamlined animals with a distinctive criss-cross pattern on the flank that is not well shown in the plate.

This is the common dolphin of the Mediterranean and the one most often illustrated in ancient Greek and Roman artwork. Like other dolphins they are vulnerable to accidental capture and drowning in fishing nets and this has been a cause for concern especially off Cornwall.

INDEX TO PLATES